Let's

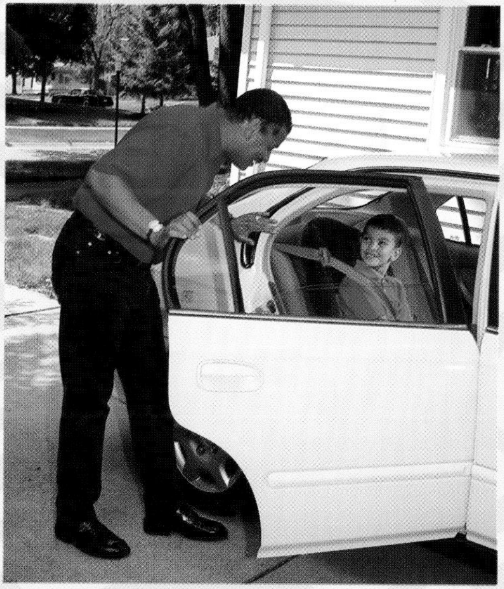

Nina Tsang

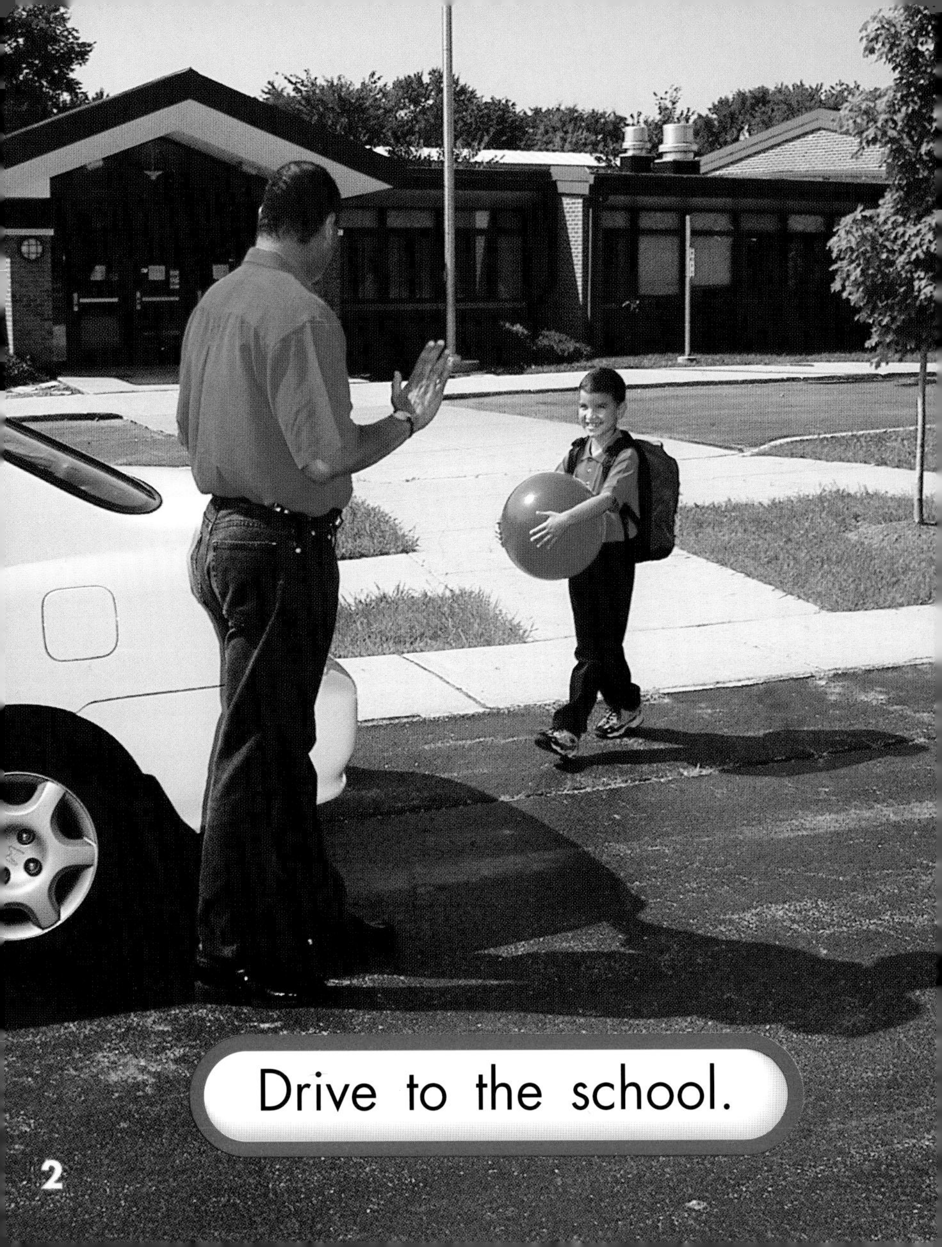

Drive to the school.

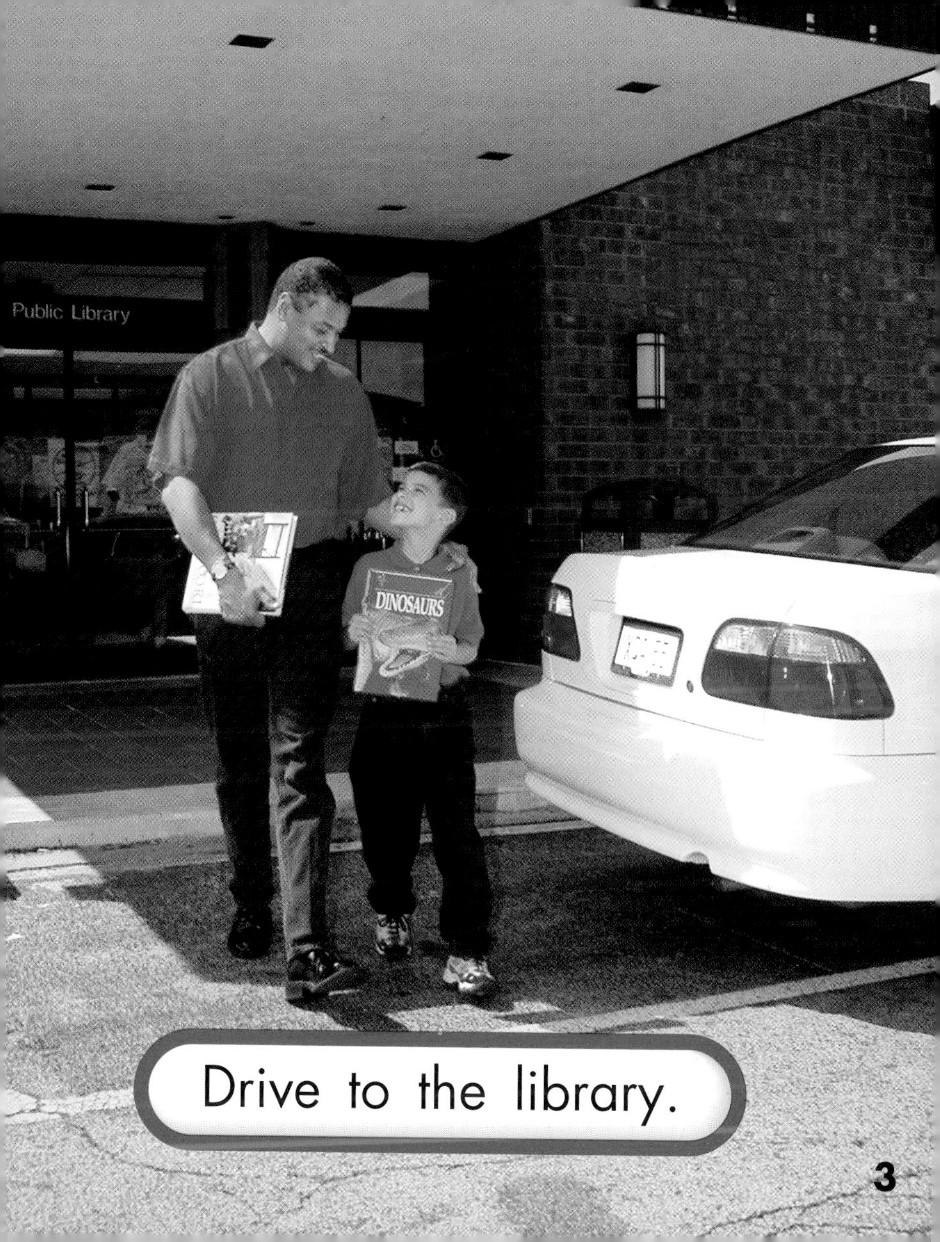

Drive to the library.

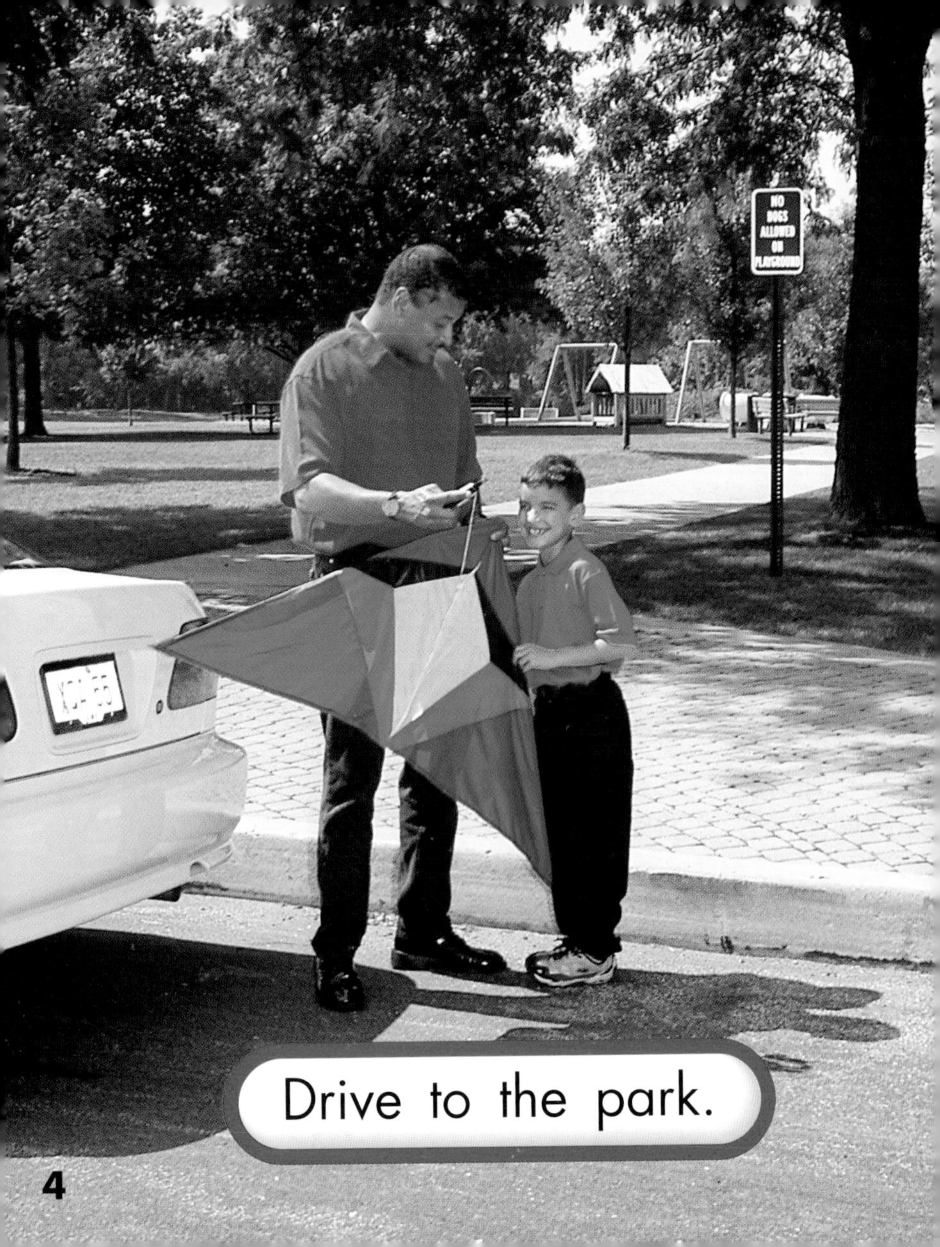

Drive to the park.

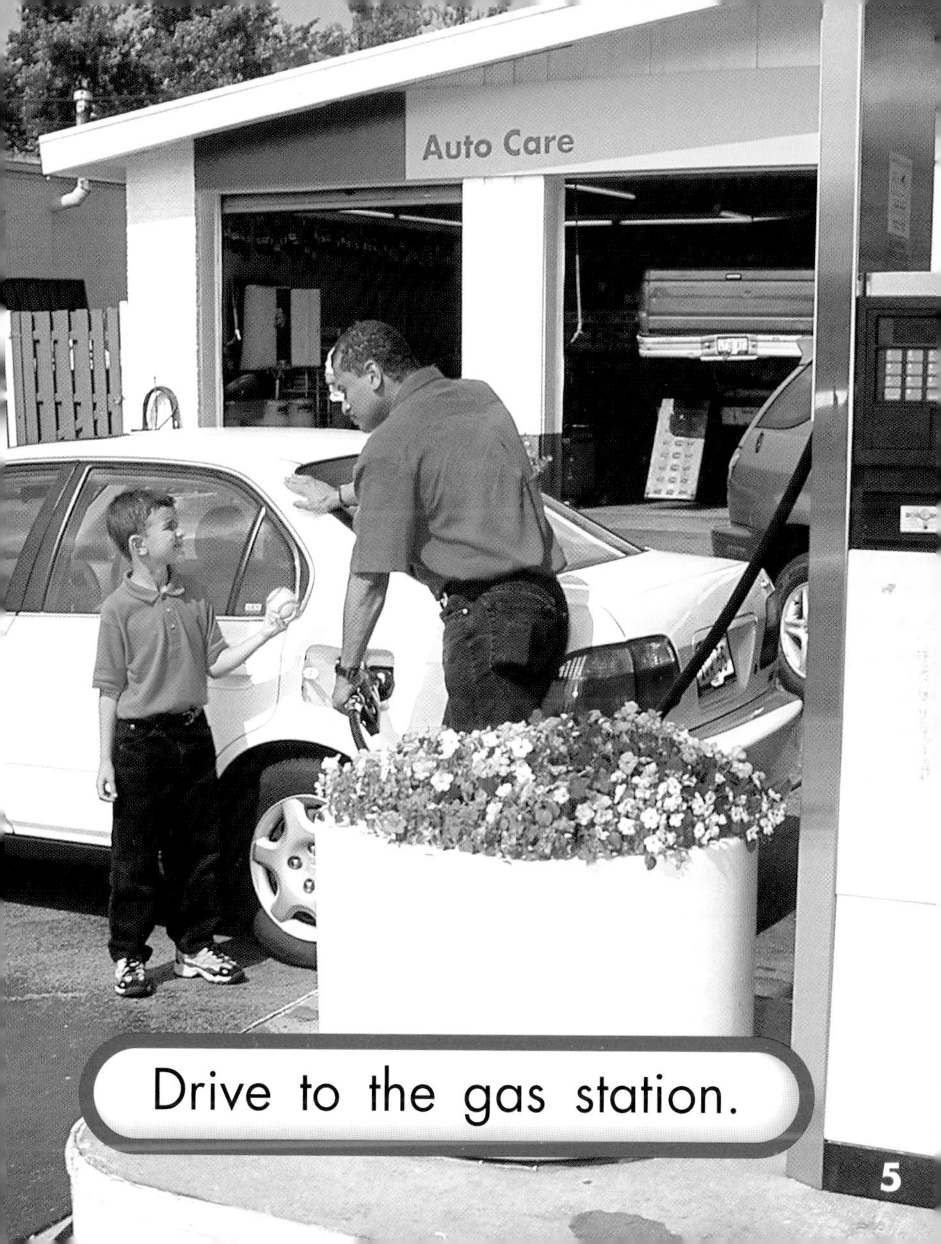

Drive to the gas station.

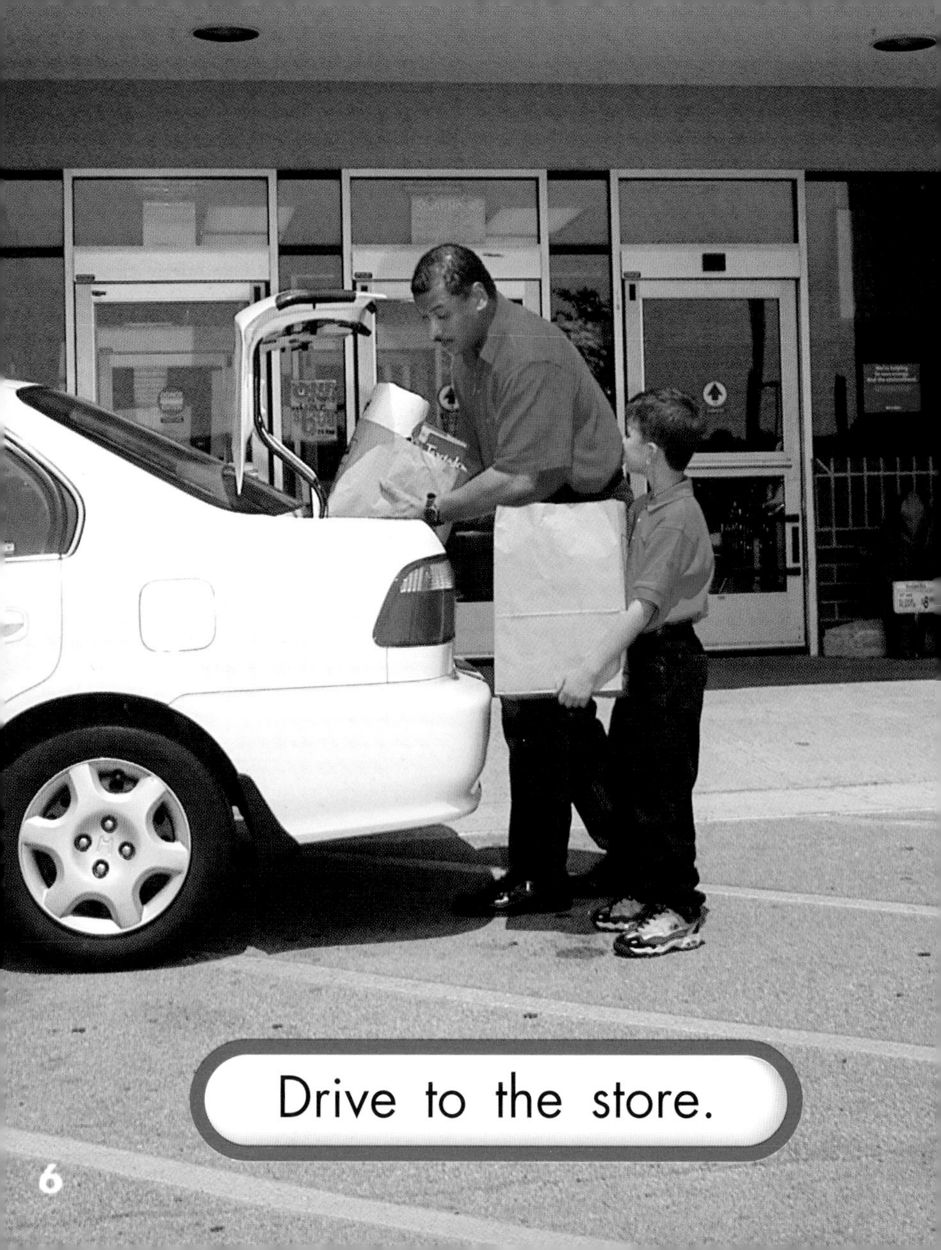

Drive to the store.

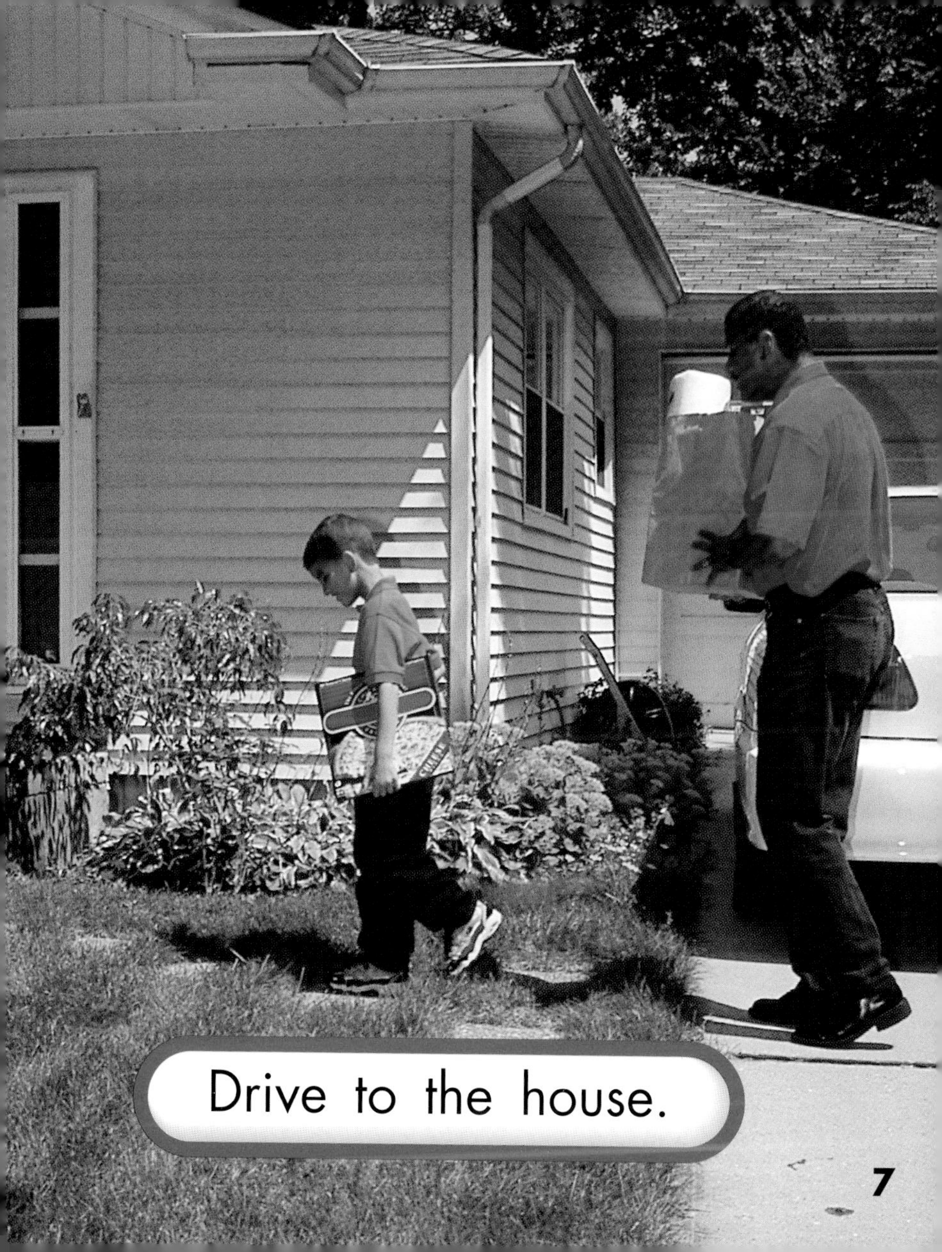

Drive to the house.

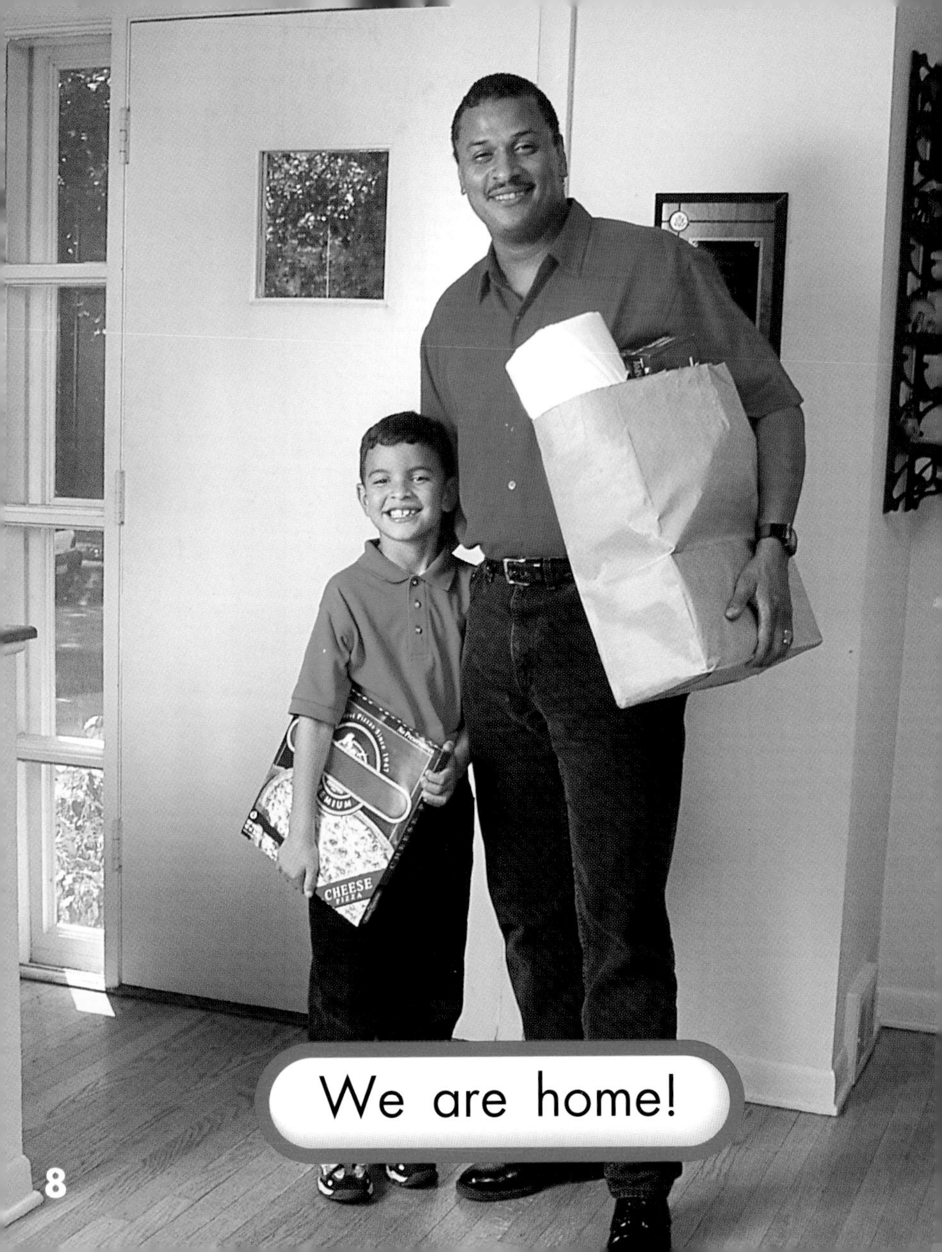

We are home!